To: The

Let LOVE ⟩ Light ⟨ your way—

D.K. Robins

Based on a true story, this book is written for dog lovers, families and readers 8 and up.

This book is based on a true story.
A SQUEAKY TOY, A LEASH, AND A PRAYER

Copyright © 2021 by dkRobins
Illustrations © 2021 by Dima Eichhorn

Designed by Justin Norman

Published by Captured
Las Vegas, NV 89117

The Library of Congress Cataloging-in-Publication Data

ISBN 978-1-7378956-0-2

This book may be purchased in bulk for promotional, educational, or business
use. Please contact your local bookseller or order at dkrobins.com.

First Edition: October 2021

Printed in the United States of America

A Squeaky Toy, a Leash, and a Prayer

by dkRobins

illustrated by Dima Eichhorn

Dedicated to all my companions.

CHAPTER 1
CHOSEN

The blackness of night filled the old barn. On this eerily still night he was all alone, for the first time. Just eight weeks old and so innocent, his brothers and sisters were gone, already adopted. His mom seemed to have disappeared before his siblings left. Fear gripped his furry little body and he trembled. Into the night he whimpered until a heavenly light shone through the broken window, wrapping him in its warmth. He curled up in

its presence. He knew he was seen and safe as he drifted off to sleep.

Blue was the last pup of his litter, the only one not chosen. His breeder woke him early the next morning with breakfast. Blue immediately started gobbling up the tasty, brown nuggets.

The breeder said, "Slow down, Blue. No competition today. It's all yours." She knelt down next to him and petted him while he ate, saying, "It won't be long, Blue. Someone will want you."

Blue waited and waited and waited all day. No one came. That evening when the breeder brought him his supper, Blue didn't budge.

"Awww... I'm sorry, Blue,

no news today," she said, "Maybe tomorrow will be the day. Don't give up, Blue. Don't give up."

Blue perked up momentarily and ate a few bites. He didn't like being alone.

That night Blue brought along his squeaky toy as he curled up in the warmth of the light, once again, blanketed by its comforting presence. He dreamed that tomorrow would be *his* day.

Little did he know that hundreds of miles away was a school teacher in Las Vegas who was searching for a Golden Retriever puppy

for her family. Early in the morning, Mrs. Robins was sipping her coffee while looking on the internet when she saw Blue's picture. She clicked on it and eagerly read the details. Blue needed a home. Instantly, she knew he was the pup for her. Mrs. Robins talked with her husband and he agreed. The teacher called Blue's breeder in Illinois and chose Blue.

After the breeder hung up the phone, she went to the barn. The sunlight was seeping through the cracks in the old boards, casting a ray of light upon Blue.

"Good morning, Blue," she said cheerfully, "I've got good news." Blue stood and wagged his tail. She went on, "A kind teacher in Las Vegas just called and chose you."

Blue immediately threw his head back and barked with joy! *Someone does want me!!* he declared.

The Breeder continued, "Blue, you're headed to Vegas!"

The last night in the old barn seemed like the longest night ever. Blue was too excited to sleep. He danced in the light until he finally wore himself out and dozed off alongside his favorite toy.

The next day Blue's breeder took him to the airport. He was going to fly on an airplane! Blue had never flown before and felt a bit anxious. His breeder gave him a big hug and told him he was going to have the adventure of a lifetime.

Blue kissed her cheek as she put him in a travel kennel with his squeaky toy. Onto the plane he went. A nice lady sat right next to him for the whole flight. Blue didn't mean to be rude, but he was so sleepy, he conked out be-

fore the plane even left the runway.

When the plane landed, Blue was greeted by the teacher's husband, Mr. Robins, and their son, Wade. He happily wagged his tail. Wade opened the kennel and picked up Blue.

"Aren't you a handsome pup," Wade remarked.

Blue wagged his whole body. He liked this boy. Blue sat on Wade's lap all the way to his new home. He felt safe and relaxed with Wade. Blue happily snuggled in close and drifted off to sleep.

It wasn't long until Wade patted his head and whispered, "Blue, we're home."

Blue took a few sideways steps in the grass and sniffed his new home. Wade chuckled as he watched him. Mr. Robins opened the front door and Blue walked right inside. A black dog and a brown dog greeted him excitedly. Sasha and Bailey sniffed him all over. Blue liked the other dogs right away. They were both herding dogs, whereas Blue was a retriever. Sasha and Bailey immediately followed Blue everywhere he went. Blue loved leading the pack.

Another boy, named Tyler, came down the stairs with an orange ball in his hands.

Blue wagged his tail and toddled straight to him.

Tyler smiled and picked up Blue, saying, "Here's our little white bear!"

Blue liked this boy, too.

But someone was missing. *Where was the school teacher?* Blue looked for her. He looked upstairs and downstairs and followed the boys outside. She wasn't in the backyard either. *Where could she be?* he wondered.

Just then, Blue heard a new voice. He ran back inside the house, and there she was! The teacher smiled and scooped him up. They looked into one another's eyes and Blue licked her right on the lips. Mrs. Robins happily hugged Blue as he rested his head on her shoulder. *She's my favorite*, he thought. Together they joined everyone outside.

Blue trotted over to the teacher's hus-

band. He was checking the water in their swimming pool. Blue was a curious boy. He wanted to check the water too. He dipped his front paw into the water.

Mr. Robins quickly picked Blue up from the edge of the pool, smiled at him and commented, "You've had enough excitement for today, Blue. We'll swim tomorrow."

Before long Blue heard a ball bouncing and ran to find Tyler and Wade dribbling that orange ball. He wanted to play too. Blue jumped up and put both his paws right on the ball.

"Our little white bear is a baller!" Tyler remarked.

Blue was so proud of himself, he could play basketball too! The boys laughed and continued to play with him.

Blue loved his family and they loved him. He knew he was right where he belonged.

That night, as he drifted off to sleep, Blue decided he liked adventures.

Very early every morning, Mr. Robins would take Blue outside to do his 'business' and then eat his breakfast. When Blue was all done, they would play tug-the-rope. Blue loved play-time. They both tugged and shook the rope. The teacher's husband was very strong, but Blue was strong too. Blue tugged with all his might, sometimes he even won. Afterwards, Mr. Robins would give Blue the best belly rubs.

At just the right time, Mr. Robins and Blue would serve coffee to the teacher while she was still in bed. Blue would wiggle all over, trying to wake her up with kisses. When she'd open her eyes, he could hardly contain himself. Mrs. Robins would laugh as she tried to hold his wiggly body. She loved her littlest fur baby.

Each day, while the teacher was at school, Blue played with Sasha and Bailey. Wherever Blue went, they followed. When Blue took a nap, they took a nap too.

All day long, Blue tried to be patient, but he wanted Mrs. Robins to come home now! Blue waited and waited and waited some more. As soon as she arrived, Blue followed her everywhere.

When she fixed supper, Blue was right there with her, just in case she needed his help.

When she watched TV, Blue watched too.

When she went for a walk, Blue went too. And if he got tired, she carried him home.

At night, Blue snuggled in close between the teacher and her husband. Sometimes, he wasn't sleepy, but he tried really hard to be still.

On Saturday mornings, Blue could barely wait to wake up the teacher and her husband. Once in a while he just couldn't help himself and woke them before the sun came up. They sipped coffee and talked with one another while he ate all his food. As soon as he was done, Blue looked at them and wondered, *isn't it playtime?* The teacher and her husband seemed to take forever. He didn't much like waiting. Blue was still learning patience. He sat very still, looking from one to the other, watching for the slightest movement toward the backdoor. Finally, they both

 stood and walked to the door. Blue ran ahead and burst through the doorway as soon as it opened. It was playtime! Blue ran and ran

around the yard. When Mrs. Robins threw his squeaky toy, Blue would run after it and wait for her to run after him. Blue liked this game, but he wasn't quite sure the teacher did. She noticed Blue didn't understand she wanted him to bring the toy back to her. So the teacher patiently taught Blue to retrieve. He learned quickly. He was a smart pup. In no time, they were both enjoying the game.

In the summertime, the teacher didn't have to go to school. She and Blue slept in until the sun woke them up. Mrs. Robins would sip her coffee by the pool while Blue took care of 'business'. Then, she would bring him his

breakfast, a *double portion* of tasty brown nuggets. Blue was getting bigger! Excitedly, he would gobble up every morsel.

Mrs. Robins and Blue spent most summer days outside together, often swimming in the pool. When she swam, Blue jumped right in and swam to her. When she was tired, Blue floated beside her on the raft. Sometimes they would even drift off to sleep. On their nightly walks, Blue no longer got tired.

But, when the school teacher got tired, he happily pulled her all the way home.

During the times

Mrs. Robins was busy, Blue played basket-
ball with Tyler and Wade as Bailey and Sasha
kept watch. After a while, the boys would get
hot and sweaty. One time, Tyler kicked off
his shoes and bolted toward the pool. All at
once he leaped high in the air and made an
enormous splash. Wade quickly chased after
Tyler, catapulting over him, and making an
even bigger splash. Blue liked this game and
thought he could make a big splash too. All

at once, he launched himself right between the two, landing with a huge puppy splash! They burst out laughing. Blue loved swimming with his boys.

Another day, the boys taught Blue how to surf on a boogie board in the pool. He wasn't quite sure at first, but the boys kept encouraging him. Blue had to be very brave.

Tyler tossed Wade Blue's squeaky toy saying, "Try putting 'Hedge' on the board."

Wade responded, "Hedge?"

Tyler smiled and said, "It *is* a hedgehog."

Wade looked at Tyler and squeaked Hedge, then he put it on the boogie board, saying, "Ok, Blue, you can do it, join Hedge."

Blue wagged his tail and took a cautious step. Wade and Tyler steadied the board and

helped him the rest of the way. Blue carefully laid down on the boogie board with Hedge while Tyler pulled him through the water us-

ing the rope. Blue lifted his head, relaxed a bit and looked around.

"Good boy, Blue!" Wade exclaimed.

Blue liked surfing.

One day Blue surprised the boys. Tyler was laying next to the pool on a chaise lounge, catching some rays; while Wade was in the water, draped over the boogie board, aimlessly drifting along. All of a sudden they heard a splash. They both looked up to see Blue swimming toward Wade. Blue grabbed the boogie board rope and pulled Wade to the side. Tyler and Wade looked at each other and dissolved into laughter. They loved Blue's new game.

Afterwards, Blue concluded that summertime with his family was a blast!

On the Fourth of July, Blue's family was having a big pool party.

That morning everyone was busy cleaning and cooking. No one was paying attention to Blue. He, along with Hedge, stretched out on the cool, kitchen floor, waiting to be noticed. Blue was getting better at waiting, even though he still didn't like it. The teacher's husband stepped over him to get his coffee. Mrs. Robins stepped over him while she was baking. The boys stepped around him while they were cleaning. Blue sighed deeply and closed his eyes, giving in to a nap.

Ding! Dong! Blue sprang to his feet and ran to the door. Mrs. Robins opened it up and there they were. . . all his aunts, uncles, cousins and grandparents. Blue was ecstatic! He wriggled all over as he greeted each guest. He knew at once he loved pool parties!

Blue swam and made huge splashes with all the big boys. When they tossed Blue's favorite toy into the pool, Blue jumped in and retrieved Hedge every time. He loved rescuing Hedge. After a while, the boys went to play basket-ball, so Blue pulled two little girls through the water on the boogie board again and

again. He quickly grew fond of Kaleysha and Brenna, and they adored him. Meanwhile, his furry friends, Bailey and Sasha, continually circled the yard keeping everyone safe.

When the girls put on swimming goggles, Blue peered at their eyes and decided he wanted goggles too. He ran over to Mrs. Robins who was busy talking with their guests. With a nice shake of his drenched body, he had her attention; actually he had everyone's attention. Mrs. Robins kneeled down and looked Blue in the eyes. He looked back at her, cocking his head one way and then the other. Standing behind him, the girls giggled. Blue looked up at them and back at Mrs. Robins. She knew just what he wanted. The teacher ran into the house and came back with his bright pink doggie goggles. She put the goggles on Blue just as three year old Anna, toddled over wearing her own pair of goggles. Blue kissed her on the cheek. The four looked adorable. Mrs. Robins had to take a picture. She held her phone sideways and said, "Everybody, say 'cheese'!" They all smiled, even Blue. Back in the water, they swam and played all afternoon.

Mrs. Robins announced, "Supper's ready!" It didn't take long for everyone to gather. They all held hands while Grandpa prayed. Blue sat quietly until Grandpa said, "Amen". Then Blue barked his own *amen*. Blue had everyone's attention again. He walked over to the buffet of food and the *adorable* girls followed. They were first in line. The girls filled their plates and sat at the little table. Blue sat very politely with the girls, watching them eat every bite and happily devour-

ing anything they dropped. When they were finished, he decided to help Mrs. Robins by cleaning up all the crumbs beneath every table. Blue enjoyed helping.

Eventually, the time came for the fireworks show. Blue's furry friends, Bailey and Sasha, quickly headed inside the house to find their comfy hiding place far away from the much

anticipated explosions. Blue and the girls huddled together on a blanket in the grass, waiting for the first fireworks to light up the sky. Blue wedged himself in the middle while little Anna plopped down on Kaleysha's lap. Blue had never seen or heard fireworks before. He was a curious boy. But before the show

even began, Blue fell fast asleep. The whole family was surprised when Blue slept right through *all* the fireworks. He was one tired pup. When the show was over, Blue was *still* sound asleep. Mrs. Robins scooped him up and held him while everyone gathered their things. Blue barely acknowledged every hug and pat as the guests left. He was happily worn out.

This was indeed Blue's favorite day.

CHAPTER 4
VACATION

Summertime flew by, and soon the teacher would be heading back to school. She had one weekend left of summer break. Mrs. Robins wanted to explore Williamson Valley, Arizona. Unfortunately, Mr. Robins needed to finish a work project and the boys had basketball practice. She and Mr. Robins agreed it would be a good trip for her and Blue.

Friday morning the teacher packed their

bags and loaded the car. She called Blue. He came trotting around the corner carrying Hedge. Mrs. Robins smiled and said, "Of course you can bring your squeaky toy." Blue had never been on vacation before. He was excited for another adventure.

Blue was riding next to Mrs. Robins in the car when all of a sudden his tummy didn't feel good. He didn't know how to tell the teacher he felt sick; just then everything came out, right in Mrs. Robins' lap.

Blue felt much better. But the teacher was not prepared for this. She parked on the side of the road, carefully opened the car door, and stepped out. Mrs. Robins brushed Blue's partially chewed dog food off her lap. Back in the car, the teacher held Blue's trembling body and assured him she would take good care of him. Blue rested his head on her shoulder, melting into her arms. He was going to be ok. Back on the road, it wasn't long until Blue dozed off.

Mrs. Robins and Blue arrived at Talking Rock Ranch after dark. They stopped at the gatehouse, and the guard gave them directions to the place where they'd be staying.

The house was tastefully decorated in western-themed rustic decor. Mrs. Robins liked it. But Blue wasn't sure what to think of this new place. It was *not* his home. It smelled different, and his boys weren't there. It was all so strange and unfamiliar. Blue felt

sad. He couldn't even eat his supper.

Blue didn't like vacation. He slept on Mrs. Robins all night long.

When he woke up the next morning, the teacher's husband wasn't there to take him outside. So Blue stared really hard at Mrs. Robins until she opened her eyes. Then he kissed her right on the lips and began prancing about.

Mrs. Robins took Blue outside to do his 'business'. Afterwards they came back inside where the teacher made breakfast for both of them. Blue was very hungry. He ate all his breakfast and was ready to play before Mrs. Robins finished her bagel. He would have to wait. Blue was patient.

Soon, Mrs. Robins and Blue left to explore the area. This was a different kind of hike than the nightly walks Blue was used to. These houses were spread far apart and looked very different from Blue's house. They were ranch-style homes with long porches extending the length of many into the desert

terrain. Blue-gray bushes, desert willows, and brown grasses covered the flatlands. The soft colors of the desert were occasionally sprinkled with bright yellow and pink flowers. The mountains were nearby, just across the main road. They were covered in an interesting mix of desert plants, various kinds of pine and spruce trees, as well as large colorful rocks. The terrain changed often as they hiked. Mrs. Robins enjoyed the amazing views. Blue, however, was still a bit unsure about this place, but he was at least curious about all the new smells.

They returned to the ranch, tired and thirsty. Blue stretched out on the dirt in front of the house, panting to cool himself off. The teacher smiled as she patted his head and unhooked his leash.

"What a great hike, Blue!" she exclaimed.

Mrs. Robins reached in her backpack and took out the garage door remote. She pressed the button and watched while the metal wheels clanged and banged as they forced the garage door up with a loud, *ARRRRR! ARRRRR!! ARRRRR!!!*

The moment Blue heard that sound, he took off! He ran and ran and ran, never looking back. *That noise was terrifying!! What kind of beast was in there?* Blue wondered. He kept running until his little legs couldn't go any farther. Blue eased to a stop and slowly turned around to check on the teacher. *But where was she?* He'd assumed Mrs. Robins was right behind him the whole time.

Unaware Blue had left, Mrs. Robins

didn't turn around until the garage door was all the way up. She was shocked when he wasn't there. *Where could he be?* she wondered. The teacher thought he must have just gone under a bush or maybe he had to take care of 'business'. But after searching everywhere close to the house, there was no sign of Blue. Mrs. Robins was puzzled. Blue had never wandered off. This was just not like him. Where was he? She'd assumed Blue was next to her the whole time.

Blue sat atop a large rock, across the main road, hidden behind a cluster of desert bushes. Blue waited and waited for the teacher. He tried to be patient, but it was really hard. *Surely, she should be here by now,* he thought. *What's taking her so long?* Blue waited some more and wondered. *What if that horrible beast has Mrs. Robins? What if she needs my help? I must find her!* Blue got up and started to walk. But which way was the ranch? Blue could not remember. So, he did the best he could and set out to find her. What he didn't know was that he was going east and the ranch was west.

The teacher walked farther and looked for Blue. She yelled for him again and again, but there was no answer. She paused and looked in every direction. Looking west, she saw an endless sea of desert browns, grays, and greens; in the opposite direction, stood mysterious and daunting mountains with a rare house built upon the rock. This place was so vast, she didn't know where to look next. Suddenly, she felt all alone.

Mrs. Robins didn't know *anyone* at Talking Rock Ranch, and her cell phone had no service. The teacher was anxious. She prayed and asked God to help her find Blue.

CHAPTER 5
GONE

Mrs. Robins decided to walk to the neighbor's house and ask if they had seen Blue. As she got closer, she spotted the neighbor raking leaves in her side yard. The teacher went and told her about Blue.

Barb put down her rake, smiled shyly and spoke quietly, "I wish I could help. But last summer I brought my dog here and she wandered off, too. I never found her. I'm really sorry."

Mrs. Robins was sorry too. The teacher thanked Barb as she walked away.

Mrs. Robins knew she would have to search harder and pray harder. She hiked across the uneven terrain and repeatedly hollered for Blue. After crossing the main road, Mrs. Robins climbed up and down the mountains all day searching for any sign of Blue. But after six difficult hours, she still couldn't find him.

Mrs. Robins was unaware that while she was searching for him, he was also searching for her. Blue had climbed over large rocks and crawled under thorn bushes and stepped very, very carefully through barbed wire fences, all the while looking for the teacher. But there was no sign of her. He was very worried. *She'd never been gone this long!*

Mrs. Robins was starting up another mountain when she heard a car horn repeatedly honking. A lady was standing next to a car waving frantically. It was the neighbor. The teacher waved back and the neighbor shouted something about Blue. Mrs. Robins ran to her.

Barb smiled and said, "I spotted your dog up the road. Get in, I'll take you there."

The teacher happily hopped into the car and rode with Barb. Mrs. Robins asked her if she had tried to call Blue.

Barb responded, "I did. He stopped in his tracks, looked back at me and then ran the other way."

Moments later Barb stopped the car and pointed to a white fence in the distance.

"He was right there fifteen minutes ago," the neighbor declared, "Good luck!"

Mrs. Robins thanked her and took off running. She was really hopeful.

The teacher looked everywhere by that fence, but didn't see Blue. She climbed over it, searched some more, and called his name. No response. He was already gone. Mrs. Robins kept on searching. She hiked farther up the mountain and climbed over three barbed wire fences, before finally reaching a house

built into the side of the mountain. The teacher knocked on the front door.

An elderly man answered the door. Mrs. Robins apologized for trespassing and told him about Blue.

He responded compassionately, "I'm really sorry about your dog. We haven't seen or heard one. But, I promise if we do, we'll notify the guard at the gatehouse."

The teacher thanked him and began the hike back down the mountain. It was getting dark now. Mrs. Robins wondered how she was going to tell her family Blue was lost. She couldn't begin to imagine telling her sons and her little nieces. Mrs. Robins agonized. She remembered assuring Blue she would take good care of him.

The teacher looked up and desperately asked God, "Where is he?"

No response. Tears spilled down Mrs. Robins' cheeks.

When she got back to the ranch, the teacher used the landline and called her hus-

band. She explained the whole story.

Mr. Robins responded, "Wow. I could never have imagined something like this would happen."

Silence filled the gap between the two. Then, Mrs. Robins told her husband she felt like it was all her fault. The teacher wept.

Mr. Robins spoke tenderly, "Honey, I'm sorry, but it wasn't your fault. You had no idea he would run away. We all know you and Blue have a special bond." Mr. Robins paused, sensing a deeper sadness growing in the love of his life. He added, "Whatever happens, please remember, you are completely loved. Nothing, including losing Blue, will ever change that. I'll be praying for both of you."

Mrs. Robins softly replied, "Thank you." As she hung up the phone, she breathed deeply and prayed. She knew it was going to be one long night.

Immediately after Mr. Robins spoke with his wife, he went outside where he found Tyler and Wade shooting hoops. Tyler had just made a basket, when he noticed Mr. Robins standing nearby.

Mr Robins said, "There's something I need to tell you boys. Your mom just called." Tyler picked up the ball as he and Wade walked over to him. Mr. Robins filled them in on the details. They were shocked to hear about Blue and their mom.

The three stood silently, each pondering his own thoughts when Wade spoke up, "Let's pray for them." Mr. Robins nodded. Tyler and he bowed their heads as Wade prayed, "God, please help my mom find Blue and please help Blue not to be afraid tonight. Amen."

Afterwards, Mr. Robins called family

and friends and told them about Blue and Mrs. Robins. They each said they'd pray, and then, they contacted more family and friends, who also agreed to pray. Tyler and Wade messaged their friends as well, and they were praying too. In minutes people from all over the country were praying for the teacher and her pup in Williamson Valley, Arizona.

Meanwhile, back at the house, Mrs. Robins prayed. She remembered reading how God surrounds us on every side, for safekeeping. She asked God to surround Blue all night long. Mrs. Robins knew God was big enough to keep her pup safe. She prayed he'd choose to.

As the teacher and the others prayed, Blue wandered aimlessly until he couldn't take another step. He was terribly hungry and awfully thirsty. *Where was Mrs. Robins?* He'd been searching and searching all day but he couldn't find her and he couldn't find his home either. Blue sniffed the air, but he still sensed nothing familiar. He felt very sad as he lowered his head. Blue never meant to lose her. He started to tremble and shake with fear. He was all alone, surrounded by mysterious shadows. That's when he remembered being inside the barn and hearing the breeder say, *"Don't give up, Blue. Don't give up."* That memory gave him fresh courage and Blue lifted his head. A familiar patch of light was just a few steps away. He made his way to the light and curled up in its comforting presence. The shadows were drowned out by the moonlight, and Blue fell fast asleep unaware of the danger lurking all around him.

CHAPTER 6

LOST

All night long Mrs. Robins got up every hour and drove up and down the road at the base of those mountains. From time to time she stopped, rolled down her window, and yelled for Blue. The mountain's silent reply was dreadfully haunting.

Away from the bright lights of Vegas, the night was intensely dark. The teacher was concerned Blue would be scared. So she turned on every light inside and outside the house to light the way home for Blue.

Mrs. Robins also decided to make a trail

for him. She cooked some hotdogs and tore them into pieces. Next, she walked from the house to the base of the mountains, dropping a piece every few steps along the way, hoping Blue would follow the scent.

When the sun came up, the teacher headed back to the spot where Blue had last been seen. She had his favorite toy and his leash. Mrs. Robins hollered, hiked, and squeaked that toy again and again, but still no response. She kept on searching.

While the teacher was hiking, she met a lady who was also hiking. This lady had heard Mrs. Robins yell and asked if she needed help. The teacher shared that she'd lost her five-month-old pup the day before, and that he'd last been seen in this specific area.

The lady responded, "Oh honey, he's gone. Last night the coyotes were out in force having a feeding frenzy right here where you're searching." She asked the teacher how she had lost her dog.

Mrs. Robins muttered, "I took his leash

off before opening the garage door, not knowing that sound would scare him and he'd take off."

The lady retorted, "I never take the leash off of my dog until we're in the house. And I never hike these mountains without my gun. This is wild country."

The teacher couldn't even speak. She was extremely sad. She walked back to the ranch.

Mrs. Robins laid on the couch and cried. She prayed and wept. The teacher asked God if this was what she must accept... If not, she pleaded with him to please give her hope.

Just then, the phone rang. It was Vicki, the owner of the house where she was staying. Mrs. Robins told her about Blue and what the lady had just said.

The owner replied, "My husband and I bring our dogs to the ranch all the time and the coyotes have never bothered them. This time of year, there's an abundance of rabbits. I can't imagine the coyotes would bother your pup."

The teacher thanked Vicki, hung up the phone, and breathed a prayer of thanks. That little bit of hope was just what she needed. Before long, she had an idea. Mrs. Robins found a stack of paper and made 'lost dog' signs, including Blue's description and the landline phone number on each. She posted them all over Talking Rock Ranch.

When she got back to the house, she noticed a small light flashing on the house phone. There was a message. She listened. Someone had seen Blue! Mrs. Robins eagerly returned the call.

A woman answered. "I just saw the sign

about your white dog. One wandered into our yard and was drinking out of our kids' pool. I tried to coax him to come to me, but he growled and backed away. The next thing I knew he took off running."

Mrs. Robins quickly asked, "How long ago?"

The woman answered, "Yesterday, about 4:00."

The teacher mumbled her thanks and hung up the phone.

Mrs. Robins fought off discouragement. While posting signs, the teacher had noticed a house on the very top of one of the high-

est mountains in the area. She knew if she could just get there, she would be able to see the whole valley. The teacher was determined. Mrs. Robins got in her car and drove around to the other side of the mountain where she found a private road that led to the house.

LOST

NAME: Blue
color: white
age: 5 months
contact: Mrs Robins
at Talking Rock Ranch
+ 1 928 776 4440

As she approached, a man came out to talk with her. The teacher apologized for trespassing and told him about Blue. Mrs. Robins asked him if he thought her five-month-old pup could have made it through the night.

He looked at her with the kindest eyes and said, "I've lost a dog to the wild here." He paused, took a deep breath, then continued, "Last summer my wife and I were sitting in the family room watching TV. Our cat was sitting on a pedestal near the screen door. All of a sudden a mountain lion pounced on that screen door and popped it open. The mountain lion reached in and grabbed our cat. Two screeches later she was gone." He let out a long sigh and added, "It's not likely, but it is possible."

Mrs. Robins handed him a flyer, thanked him, and sadly walked away.

CHAPTER 7

HELP

The teacher drove back down the mountain with a heavy heart.

She arrived at the gatehouse and asked the guard the same question, "Do you think it's possible my five-month-old pup could have made it through the night?"

The guard looked her right in the eyes and said, "Ma'am, the coyotes would eat your pup."

Mrs. Robins swallowed the painful lump in her throat as she drove on. Back at the ranch, she tried to pray, but she kept on crying. God heard her anyway.

Suddenly, the doorbell rang. The teacher sprang to her feet, startled from her grief. She opened the door. It was a different lady, someone else she'd never met.

Jan took one look at the school teacher and said, "Don't you dare give up! I'm going to help you find your pup."

Jan had a plan. She immediately e-mailed all the people living in Talking Rock Ranch and then said to the teacher, "Come on! We're going off-roading!"

The teacher got in Jan's truck and they drove up and down the backroads of the valley, searching and yelling for Blue. At their first stop, Jan handed Mrs. Robins her binoculars to use. The teacher stood and looked in every direction. But no sign of Blue. They continued down the road, stopping regularly for a closer look. The teacher felt encouraged, but

even after sev-
eral hours, they
still didn't find
Blue. Jan took
her back to the
house.   Mrs.
Robins   was
very   thankful
for all of her help. Before Jan left, she loaned
the teacher her binoculars for the rest of the
day.

Mrs. Robins walked around the outside
of the house continuing to look for any sign
of Blue when she was startled by a familiar car sound. She came around the corner of
the house just as Tyler and Wade drove into
the driveway. They surprised their mom and
wrapped her in a big hug.

Tyler said, "We're going to help you find
Blue, Mom."

Wade cheerfully added, "We brought plen-
ty of water, and an extra leash too."

Mrs. Robins smiled. She was so happy to

see her boys. She told them about Jan's plan while they filled their backpacks with water and snacks. They each chose a different area to search and agreed on a time to meet back at the house.

Tyler drove each one to their specific area. Mrs. Robins got out of the car first. She searched the flatlands to the north covered with dense desert brush bordering a well-manicured golf course. Occasionally, a rabbit would scamper across the fairway and into the brush. Each time the teacher saw movement, her heart quickened with hope. She walked on, continuing to observe the landscape, interrupting the silence every so often with the sound of Blue's squeaky toy.

Tyler dropped Wade off next. Wade explored the ditches on both sides of the mountain road. He found a long branch and used it to push the tall grass aside as he trudged through it. Wade checked inside the culverts beneath the road. At the far end of the second culvert, he saw something move beneath

a tangled mound of branches and leaves. He crept closer and quietly called, "Blue?" Suddenly, a head popped through the top of the mound. Wade gasped as a small fox locked eyes with his, neither moved a muscle. Then instantly, the fox disappeared into the bramble, and Wade continued his search.

Tyler parked the car alongside the road not too far away from his little brother. He slung his backpack over his shoulders and began to climb up the rugged mountain. The late afternoon sun beat upon him. After a while, he paused for a drink and thought about how terribly thirsty Blue must be. Tyler looked down the mountain to check on his brother. He spotted Wade's red hair further down the road from the place he'd dropped him off. *Good. He had made progress,* Tyler noted. He turned to continue the climb when he detected movement. He had a feeling he was not alone. Tyler intently scanned the web of desert plants and rocks below him. Then he saw it. . . two eyes. . . no. . . four eyes looking back at him. Coyotes! He was being followed. Tyler took a deep breath and reached down for a rock. He yelled and threw the rock to spook the animals. It worked! They ran off, at least for now. Tyler had to get down the mountain. He was not only searching for Blue but now he had his eyes peeled for coyotes as well.

After nearly five hours, the three of them arrived back at the house exhausted and discouraged. Wade fell asleep on the couch. Tyler was hungry and left to pick up pizza for the family. Mrs. Robins laid down Blue's leash and squeaky toy. She hadn't seen Blue for over thirty hours.

The teacher headed out the back door alone and walked slowly. There was a heaviness in each step. She was talking with God. Mrs. Robins said, "I just don't get it. You've given me sign after sign to encourage me, but no Blue. I know you don't always answer the way we think you should or the way we want you to. . ." Her voice became softer and softer and then stopped. Mrs. Robins cried as she let go of Blue in her heart and gave him to God.

Gradually, she took a few steps, then paused and boldly asked God for one more sign. She said, "I have seen all kinds of things today, but I haven't seen a single butterfly. If there's a thread of hope left, please give me a butterfly."

But God didn't give her a butterfly.

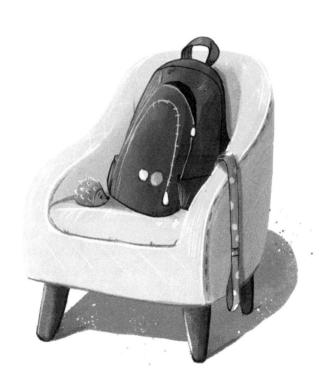

CHAPTER 8
LOVE

The eerie stillness of the night settled all around Mrs. Robins as she began the painful walk back to the ranch. In the distance, she could see that the porch light was on. The teacher was worn-out. She slowly made her way to the light. As she approached the deck, her eyes stopped and focused upon a small copper butterfly.

She looked up and whispered, "Is that you, God?"

Mrs. Robins took a couple more steps and saw a huge copper butterfly.

She smiled and said, "Ok, God, I'll hold

on."

The teacher climbed the stairs of the long deck and walked to the end facing the mountains. She stared up at those mountains she and her sons had hiked.

Then, Mrs. Robins whistled into the dark night and waited. Her ears strained for a response. Her eyes pleaded for a glimpse of Blue. Her heart ached for an answer. All of a sudden, she heard a faint bark! She whistled again... another faint bark!!

Mrs. Robins ran into the family room and woke Wade. She was pulling him outside with her, just about to whistle again, when the house phone rang.

It was the man from the house on top of the mountain. He said, "I'm so sorry about your pup. But, I have to let you know that right now, on top of the highest mountain, there is a pup and he is barking and crying! We tried to reach him but we didn't have flashlights. We have no idea whether he's yours, but I just had to let you know."

The teacher begged him for directions. The man gave her directions that would get her as close to the top of that mountain as possible. She thanked him and hung up the phone.

Mrs. Robins and Wade opened every drawer and cabinet in the house until they found two flashlights. On the way out the door, the teacher grabbed Blue's leash and Wade snatched a golf club for protection. They knew it was going to be dangerous.

They got in the car and Mrs. Robins turned the key. They were almost out of gas. Mrs. Robins and Wade looked at each other. They knew they were going to have to pray their way to the top of that mountain.

They took the main road that led them around to the backside of the mountains. Af-

ter some time, they turned off the paved road onto a rugged gravel road that wound precariously upwards through the desert brush. Mrs. Robins prayed as they crept over the uneven terrain while Wade had his eyes peeled for the unmarked little lane  that would take them to the top.

"There it is!" he cried, pointing to the right.

Mrs. Robins turned onto the rocky, narrow lane and they inched their way straight up the mountain. It seemed like it took forever; then the road abruptly came to an end. Mrs. Robins put the car in park while Wade rolled down his window and called out as loud as he could, "BLUE!"

From on top of the mountain someone answered, "What's his name?"

Wade, who was terrified of heights, suddenly had no fear. He leaped out of the car and scaled that mountain like a superhero!

Mrs. Robins stood next to the car and waited. Then, finally came the words her

heart had so longed to hear: "We got him!!"
Wade announced.

Mrs. Robins raised her eyes and her hands
to God, who against ALL odds had protected
her pup!

In that moment God reminded Mrs. Robins that her crazy love for her pup was nothing compared to His crazy love for her. . . for

everyone, including Blue. She smiled from deep in her heart as tears of joy streamed down her face.

Blue and Wade came down that mountain, and the celebration began. Wade was laughing and beaming as he tried to contain Blue's squirming body. Blue was wiggling, barking, and crying simultaneously. Mrs. Robins scooped him up, and he kissed her again and again.

The teacher looked up to see an old man helping a woman slowly down the mountain. The headlights from her car illuminated the pair. She recognized the man from the house that was built into the side of the mountain. Mrs. Robins was stunned! The man's eyes met the teacher's, they were both filled with tears. Once he and his wife made it down that peak, they joined the happy crew. He smiled at Mrs. Robins and Wade.

He explained, "My wife and I hadn't hiked these mountains for ten years! But when we heard a puppy's cry, we thought he might be yours. So we set out to find him. It was daylight when we left our house and neither of us thought to grab a flashlight." He paused to look at his wife and smiled.

She smiled back and she continued, "We nearly turned back a time or two as darkness settled around us. But the light of the moon shone on the path and his whimper kept beckoning us on. It was quite a journey."

The man went on, "When we finally found him he was trembling with fear, all tuckered out. He let my wife sit next to him and comfort him. I handed her the strap off my binoculars and she laced it through his collar like a leash. We've been huddled here together ever since."

The teacher was amazed! The three of them courageously waited to be found for nearly two hours. Mrs. Robins, Wade, and Blue thanked them again and again. Beneath the starry sky, they all celebrated.

Little did they know that from the safety

of his living room, the man from the house on top of the mountain was looking through his binoculars, watching the scene unfold. Silhouetted against the light of the moon, he saw what appeared to be a magical celebration, unlike anything he'd ever seen before. He knew she had found him.

CHAPTER 9
YES

Everyone piled in the car, as they marveled at all that had happened. They were aglow, overwhelmed with joy! The car could not contain their laughter and delight. Right in the middle of them all, wiggled Blue, the happiest pup on the mountain. What an adventure they'd all had, including Blue—*the adventure of a lifetime!*

Although they had hardly any gas, they all knew God would get them to the couple's house. And, of course, He did. Mrs. Robins and Wade were shocked at how long a drive it was to their home. Once again they were amazed at the amount of courage it took to hike that distance in these mountains at night. The man pointed ahead, directing the teacher to turn left. She turned onto a path lined with a canopy of trees taking them deeper into the mountains. As they came around a bend, they coasted into the couple's driveway where hugs were exchanged and grateful words shared. Before they left, God had one more surprise for them; the man went into his garage and came out with a gas can. The teacher was speechless and grateful as he put gas in their car.

Blue sat on Wade's lap on the drive back to the ranch. Mrs. Robins and Wade were bursting with joy at the unbelievable way God had answered their prayers. They turned into Talking Rock Ranch and stopped at the gatehouse.

The teacher looked the guard right in the eyes and said, "We got him!!"

The guard stuck his head inside the car. Blue and the guard were nose to nose. The baffled look on the guard's face was priceless.

Mrs. Robins drove into the driveway of the house, honking and honking. Tyler ran toward the car. The teacher held Blue's leash and opened the car door. Out came Blue, wriggling all over and whimpering again as Tyler hugged him.

The celebration continued. Jan with the plan heard the honking and stopped by.

She took one look at Blue and said, "We're going to have to name that mountain, 'Blue's Mountain'."

Blue threw his head back and barked in agreement.

The teacher called her husband, the boys messaged their friends, and the good news was passed around to family members and groups of people she didn't even know were praying for her and her pup.

Three little boys at a sleepover had been praying. Grandparents in Iowa had been praying. A prayer group in Tennessee had been praying. A Bible study group in Las Vegas had been praying. Three girls on a beach in California had been praying. Aunts, uncles, and cousins; all had been praying.

God heard every prayer. And He chose to answer, "Yes."

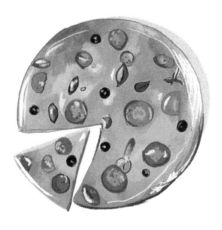

Hearts overflowed with joy as stomachs were filled with pizza. Blue was happily devouring a bowl of tasty brown nuggets when he noticed his favorite toy across the room waiting for him. Blue retrieved Hedge and happily squeaked away. It wasn't long until a contented tiredness blanketed Blue, his boys, and Mrs. Robins. They could finally rest.

Soon, they headed to bed. During the night, Blue was awakened by the heavenly light streaming through the window. In its presence, Blue knew he was loved. He sighed deeply and nestled in closer to Mrs. Robins, grateful he had finally found her.

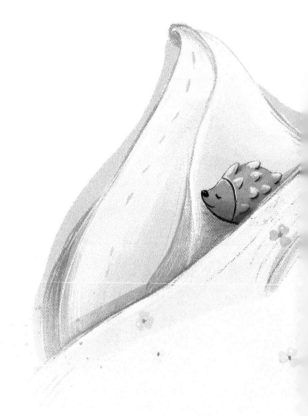

CHAPTER 10
HOME

The following morning, the boys and Mrs. Robins packed their things and loaded up both cars. Blue, of course, brought Hedge and quickly hopped in the backseat with Wade. Mrs. Robins turned the key and smiled, remembering who put gas in her car. She drove through Talking Rock Ranch one last time with Tyler following in his car. Before they even passed the gatehouse, Blue was sound asleep. A couple of times during the drive home, Mrs. Robins stopped for gas. Blue would momentarily lift his sleepy little head and glance out the window. His ears would perk up as he watched Tyler putting

gas in the cars. But when he looked past him, he saw nothing familiar, and would lay his head right back down on Wade's lap.

After a while, they stopped for an early supper. This time Blue sat up and looked around. Tyler got out of his car and Wade got out too. They both tried to coax Blue to join them, but he was not budging. Tyler had an idea. He reached in the car and grabbed Hedge while Wade held Blue's leash. As soon as Blue spotted Hedge in Tyler's hand, he stood up, wagged his tail, and hopped right out of the car. Blue smiled as he gently took Hedge from Tyler. Then, he freely and happily walked around with *his* boys.

Meanwhile, Mrs. Robins bought supper. She spotted Blue and the boys walking nearby in a small grassy area. The teacher found a blanket in the car and joined them. Blue sniffed out the perfect spot for a picnic. Mrs. Robins spread the blanket on the ground. Everyone sat down, with Blue choosing to sit right in the middle. Blue liked picnics. They bowed their heads and gave thanks to God. Together they said, "Amen", as Blue barked his own *amen*. Mrs. Robins passed out the food. Blue tried a bit of everything, deciding french fries were his favorite. When everyone was finished, Blue helped the boys clean up. Then, once again he and Hedge curled up on Wade's lap in the backseat.

Beneath the light of the moon, they drove the remaining miles. The final hour passed quickly as

they each quietly reflected upon the previous day's events. Before long, the lights of Vegas were in view. The teacher graciously whispered her thanks to God.

In a short time, they turned into *their* driveway.

Mrs. Robins reached into the back seat and patted Blue's head saying, "We're home, Blue."

He stood and stretched, then looked out the window. His tail began wagging and he barked with joy. Mr. Robins came outside to greet them. Wade opened the door as Blue immediately picked up Hedge and leaped out of the car. He trotted over to the teacher's husband where all at once he dropped Hedge and rolled over onto his back. Mr. Robins laughed and gave Blue the best belly rub!

Bailey and Sasha met Blue at the front door. He kept barking and barking, telling them all about his big adventure. They followed his every bark and exchanged curious looks. Tyler and Wade were amused as they

followed the furry pack.

Mr. and Mrs. Robins' eyes met. Mr. Robins held his wife in a warm embrace. They smiled and shared a tender moment. The teacher picked up Hedge, then together the two joined the others.

When Blue walked out the back door, he found there was a party waiting for him. All of his aunts, uncles, cousins and grandparents came to celebrate God's answer to their prayers. Blue's 'adorable little girls' were the first to greet him. They immediately surrounded him with the best group hug. He kissed each one right on the lips. Then everyone said at once, "WELCOME HOME, BLUE!!"

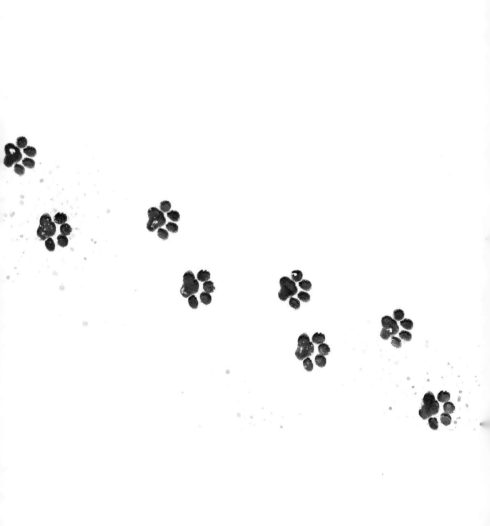